Science and the Vikings

Stephen Ernest Harding
Ridder Første, Norge

The Hakon Hakonsson Lecture, 2016
delivered at the
Valhalladrome, Viking Experience Theatre,
Barrfields, Largs,
Thursday, September 1, 2016

Largs & District Historical Society, 2017

Published by the Largs Historical Society

Largs Museum

2 Manse Court

Largs KA30 8AW

and in conjunction with NCMH Outreach

www.nottingham.ac.uk/ncmh

Printed by Largs Printing Co., 120 Main Street, Largs.

Cover Design: Stuart Ballantyne,

adapted from an original design by *ArniEin*

ISBN 978-1-5272-0706-6

My Lords, Ladies and Gentlemen –

This evening you have in front of you for this year's Hakon Hakonsson Lecture neither a historian nor an archaeologist, but rather a scientist. A scientist who has been interested in the Vikings ever since he discovered that the name of the football team he has supported since the age of five was Norse in origin – this is Tranmere Rovers. For years I have been saying that Tranmere is unique by being the only team in the English Football League with a Norwegian Viking name[1]. That was fine until last year when, regrettably, the team were relegated out of the Football League completely! So now we operate in the National Vanarama Conference.

Of course, *research* into the Vikings has now become multi- or inter-disciplinary, with many subjects contributing. History, Linguistics and Archaeology are still the lead subjects, but Science and its various branches are now making an important contribution. So this lecture will be about *Science and the Vikings*, and will include some speculation – informed speculation – that the Vikings may have had some scientific skills themselves.

It is a great honour for me to be following a line of very distinguished lecturers. The very first Hakon Hakonsson Lecture was delivered in 1981 by the great Magnus Magnusson and was appropriately titled *Hakon the Old – Hakon Who?*[2] Not only was Magnus a highly acclaimed broadcaster with the BBC, famous for *Mastermind* of course, but he was also famous for other popular and scholarly series such as *Chronicle* and *Vikings!* – the latter, in my opinion, still by far the best series made on Vikings, unsurprisingly, since Magnus was one of their descendants. Magnus was a distinguished Viking scholar and, with Hermann Palsson, translated several of the Icelandic sagas into English.

Sixteen years ago he wrote the foreword to a book I myself had written about the Vikings in the north west of England, called *Ingimund's Saga* (**Fig. 1**). How did this come about? Well, I wrote to him – his address was in the phone book so was very easy to find – asking if he would do this, expecting a reply saying he would be too busy. This was not the case, and within two or three days a wonderful reply came back saying, "Steve I would be delighted to write a foreword, and what's more, if you send me the draft, I would look through it and make some suggestions". I think he was making sure that what he was putting his name to was OK!

---

[1] From Old Norse *trani* (cranebirds/ herons) and *melr* (sandbank)
[2] Magnus Magnusson (1982) *Hakon the Old – Hakon Who?* Largs Historical Society. The book has recently been reprinted by the Society

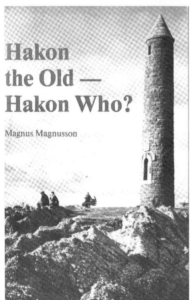

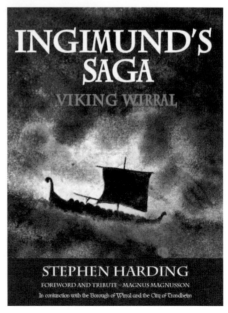

Figure 1. Magnus, the 1st Hakon Hakonsson Lecture - published by the Largs & District Historical Society, and Ingimund's Saga.

And sure enough I sent him the draft and within a few days a package containing the manuscript came back. The first thing to come out of the package was a waft of strong tobacco – apparently Magnus was a great pipe smoker – and then followed the manuscript: this was covered in green ink. He had used up an entire weekend going through it from cover to cover making a comprehensive and exhaustive set of helpful suggestions. Magnus was very proud of his Viking roots and was more than happy to help those who shared his passion.

So that was the year 2000. And now, in 2016, I have updated that book to take into account the recent archaeological discoveries, the DNA work, and all the exciting developments that have been happening in the northwest over the last 16 years. The third edition of *Ingimund's Saga* duly came out on September 1st – the day of this Lecture – courtesy of Chester University Press.

As I am sure many of you know, very sadly Magnus passed away in 2007. I contacted Magnus's daughter Sally to ask if it would be acceptable to go ahead with the new edition, and if it would be appropriate to include the original foreword from Magnus together with a tribute. She was delighted and said, "My dad would be absolutely thrilled".

One of the very many achievements of Magnus was to dispel any mistaken impression that the public may have had, that the Vikings were just a bunch of adventurous but violent and aggressive opportunists, and there was nothing much else about them. This was far from the truth and he, more than anybody else in the media, was able to show just what an articulate commonwealth of northern peoples the Vikings were.

They were adventurous raiders, yes, but they were also great navigators and explorers. They were great craftsmen, and their skills in building seafaring boats and shipping – all based on a "clinker" or overlapping planks style – was unparalleled.

They were great lawyers: the word law comes from an Old Norse (ON) word *lǫg* (pronounced lawg) – and they were great parliamentarians with their Assemblies or Things (ON: Þing). In the Wirral peninsula where I come from we have a site called Thingwall where the Vikings had their Assembly. Magnus had this great ability to convey to us this wonderfully diverse spectrum of attributes of the Vikings. So the question now is, were they scientists too?

I. SUNSTONES AND VIKINGS

This leads us to explore the speculation that the Vikings may also have been using science to some degree when navigating the seaways. To guide them along their way they would have used the position of the Sun during the daytime, along with known coastal landmarks, and seaborne bird life. They would have used the stars at night: on board for the long journeys it is possible they had someone who could recognise patterns of stars in the sky and use them as a directional aid (a Viking equivalent of Patrick Moore or Brian Cox!). For long journeys there has been some recent speculation that they were able to use special birefringent crystals in cloudy conditions when the position of the sun was not visible. "Sunstones" are certainly mentioned in the Sagas ... but no one had much of an idea what these might have been, or what they were used for – until now.

It so happens that across Scandinavia, and also in Iceland, there can be found crystals of calcium carbonate appropriately known as "Iceland Spar", a transparent form of calcite. These crystals have a special property called *birefringence* i.e. the ability to form a double image of an object[3]. Light is a wave form with two components or *vectors* moving in the same direction but at right angles to each other, and if these two vectors interact with a medium in different ways, then you get two images when light passes through.

Figure 2 shows our own family calcite crystal. It is actually now the property of my Granddaughter!... and she has kindly loaned this beautiful object back to us for this evening. You can see two images of the words *OPTICAL CALCITE* appearing. The intensity of the two images and their position depends on where the crystal is in relation to the position of the Sun in the sky, and where you are with respect to the Geographic North. So could these Iceland Spar crystals be the sunstones referred to in the Sagas? And could the Vikings have used these to navigate in cloudy conditions?

To demonstrate this let us simulate cloudy conditions. Let us take an overhead projector with the light source representing the sun, and use a transparency with a single square drawn on, and project it onto a grey wall (appropriate for cloud!). Now, if I place the crystal over the square, you can see two squares or images, and, if I rotate the crystal slowly, you can see that one square remains fixed, but the position and intensity of the second square changes. I can simulate thicker cloud by putting a piece of lens tissue in between the lamp and the crystal. If you train your eyes you can still just about see the two images.

---

[3] Harding SE (2016) https://theconversation.com/did-the-vikings-use-crystal-sunstones-to-discover-america-53836

Figure 2. Icelandic Spar/ optical calcite and projection of the crystal & double image formation of a drawing of a square (arrowed) using the lamp in an overhead projector to represent the sun. Location: *Valhalladrome.*

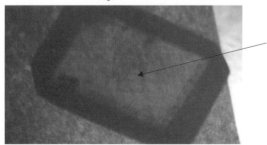

If lens tissue – mimicking thicker cloud - is inserted in the path of the beam, the double image is still visible.

The suggestion has been made that a crystal could have been mounted by a Viking Age craftsman on some sort of frame with a dial, and, under clear conditions of normal daylight, an observer would have recorded the *position* (relative to the sun and/or known landmarks) and *relative intensity* of the two images in order to calibrate the dial. Then, when it was cloudy, simply by recording the position and intensity, and then checking against the calibrated dial, our observer could in principle work out where on the earth's surface he was. So it might have been possible for a skilled observer to use such a device as a navigational aid under cloudy conditions. Further research is going on.

This is all speculation at the moment, of course, and will remain so until someone finds one on an excavated Viking ship: and although I would dearly love this to be true, I am afraid that it has yet to happen. So there you have some speculation about the scientific expertise of the Vikings – informed speculation perhaps – as these birefringent crystals are indeed found in relative abundance in Scandinavia.

II. SCIENTIFIC RESEARCH ON THE VIKINGS

For the rest of my presentation I should like to talk about how Science is giving us information about the Vikings themselves. In order to reinforce what I said earlier: Viking research is no longer the preserve of historians, linguists (including onomasts i.e. experts on place names) and archaeologists but is multi- or inter-disciplinary. Science, and its various branches, is now making an important contribution to our understanding of these people, who, for so many of us, are an important part of our ancestry[4].

Firstly, from *Physics* our consideration of sunstones is an example from the branch of Physics known as Optical Physics, but further examples we will consider include metal detectors and geophysical equipment (from another branch of Physics – Electricity and Magnetism), and the use of high energy lasers – Laser Physics – for the restoration of valuable artefacts from the Viking Age. We consider also *Chemistry*, and the wonderful contribution chemists are making in terms of the use of either stable or radioactive chemical isotopes, and the use of Polymer Chemistry in trying to save and preserve the Oseberg Viking ship and its important artefacts; finally we consider *Biology* and the considerable input research into DNA and Genetics is providing.

---

[4] A recent example is a collection of papers about the Vikings in NW England: Harding SE, Griffiths D, Royles E editors (2014) *In Search of Vikings. Interdisciplinary Approaches to the Scandinavian Heritage of North-West England*, CRC Press, Boca Raton, USA

III.   PHYSICS AND THE VIKINGS

Way back in the 1970s I did a Physics degree at University, and when I chose to do this I had absolutely no idea how relevant this was to Vikings; and indeed it will be really exciting if the hypothesis, speculation, informed speculation, whatever you like to call it, about the sunstones and their link with optical calcite is proven. But that is all it is at the moment – speculation. So let us look at more solid, proven contributions.

Metal Detectors

Now take, for example, the fascinating case of metal detectors. These devices can set you back between about £300 to over £1,000, depending on how sophisticated they are, but this is still in the affordable range for many enthusiasts. This accessibility has led to hordes of amateur enthusiasts continually trawling around Britain for buried treasure: and they are doing great work. Using these types of simple physical equipment, metal detector enthusiasts have literally found thousands of objects – many from the Viking Age – with this technology. Metal detectors work on a very simple physical principle (**Fig. 3**). You have an oscillating electrical current which sets up an alternating magnetic field, and then, if the magnetic field impacts on any metal objects hidden under the surface, this alternating magnetic field sets up its own electrical current in the metal – we call this an eddy current – which then produces its own magnetic field. This then interferes with the original magnetic field, and this disturbance is picked up by the detector either as a light signal or a sound.

It is thus possible to detect hidden metal objects to a reasonable depth, and this has led to many remarkable finds. In the past some important finds might not have been reported, because enthusiasts have been hesitant of declaring their finds for a number of reasons, including a fear of confiscation without compensation or recognition. However that situation has completely changed, and there are clear regulations set up in Scotland, England and Wales which protect the discoverers and encourages them to declare their finds. In Scotland this is the *Treasure Trove Law,* and in England and Wales the *Portable Antiquities Scheme* (PAS).

One very recent and spectacular recent find – done through Treasure Trove - was by a metal detectorist from Ayrshire, Derek McLennan, and colleagues at a location in Galloway, a region of south west Scotland once settled by the Vikings. The presence of the place name *Tinwall* – an Old Norse name meaning "Assembly Field" – confirms that the settlements there were once significant.

Principle of Metal
Detectors

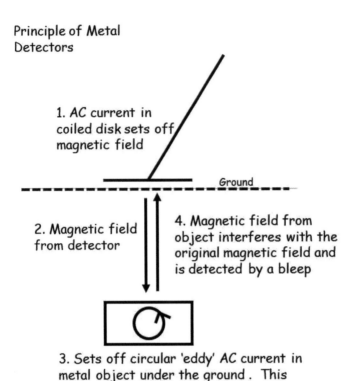

1. AC current in
coiled disk sets off
magnetic field

Ground

2. Magnetic field
from detector

4. Magnetic field from
object interferes with the
original magnetic field and
is detected by a bleep

3. Sets off circular 'eddy' AC current in
metal object under the ground . This
current sets off its own magnetic field

Figure 3. Metal detectors and their use by amateur enthusiasts are making a huge
contribution, together with the responsible reporting of finds through the Treasure
Trove or Portable Antiquities Schemes. The principle behind the technique – shown in
this simplified diagram - is based on the relationship between alternating electric
currents and magnetic fields.

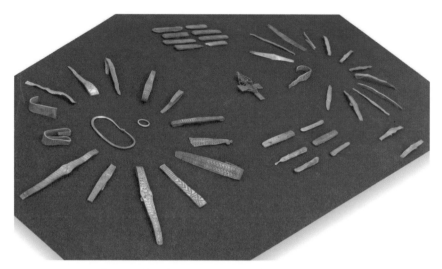

Figure 4. Some important Viking Age finds recently made by metal detector enthusiasts. Above: Part of the Galloway Hoard (discovered 2014), reported to the Treasure Trove scheme in Scotland, including arm bands, ingots and a silver cross. Some of the treasure may have originally derived from a Monastery.
Below left: a Thor amulet (Thurcaston); Centre: Silver ingots (Breedon); Right: Olaf Guthfrithsson Coin (Neston). The coin was subsequently discovered by metal analysis to be an elaborate fake.

Another find – again by a metal detector enthusiast – which has recently been catalogued in the Portable Antiquities Scheme by Finds Liaison Officer Wendy Scott - was made not far from where I now live in the East Midlands of England, near a place called Thurcaston, deep into what used to be the English Danelaw. The Danelaw was that part of England essentially lying to the East of what is now the A5 (Watling Street), controlled and settled by the Danes in the 9th Century. The Danelaw is full of names that derive from the Vikings, including my village of East Leake, which preserves the Old Danish *laek* (stream), and even the village I got married in – Thurnby "the settlement with/near the thorn bushes". Thurcaston preserves the name of the Scandinavian man *Þorketill,* and here a hoard of coins from the Viking Age was found together with an impressive amulet of the Norse god Thor. Three further Viking Age coins (East Anglian pennies) have recently been found nearby at Loughborough and Melton. These finds – all by enthusiasts – together with silver ingots used by Viking settlers found (near a monastery!) at Breedon, certainly point to a thriving bullion economy, at least in this part of the Danelaw.

The Neston "Olaf Guthfrithsson" coin: Electron Probe Microarray Analysis

Are finds always genuine? Neston, on the Wirral peninsula, is another area steeped in Viking tradition, and one of only two areas in England with a *definite* Thingwall place name (the other being across the Mersey in West Derby)[5]. This is where my roots are and where I grew up. In 1995 a metal detector enthusiast found a silver ingot from the Viking Age, similar to those found at Breedon, and in 2007 another enthusiast found a coin attributed to Olaf Guthfrithsson, a Dublin-based Viking King who fought in the Battle of Brunanburh in AD 937, and later became King of Northumbria at York. This was a huge battle in which the Vikings and Scots fought side-by-side against their common enemy – the Angles and Saxons from *Angle-land* "England". Of course quite a few years later the Vikings and Scots were fighting against each other – at the Battle of Largs (AD 1263). Although there is still some dispute as to where the Battle of Brunanburh took place, the vast majority of experts accept the battle took place on Wirral – Brunanburh is the old name for modern Bromborough. The place of escape of Olaf's forces - as recorded in the contemporary Anglo-Saxon account of the battle – was from *Dingesmere*, which I suggested in 2004[6] to my colleague Dr. Paul Cavill at the English Place-Name Society as the "Things mere" the waterway or wetland overlooked or controlled by the Thing (the place of Assembly at Thingwall – the symbol of Scandinavian power).

---

[5] Evidence for other locations has been presented such as at Little Langdale in the Lake District. There are several in Scotland/Scottish Isles & of course Tynwald in the Isle of Man

[6] http://www.nottingham.ac.uk/ncmh/dna/Brunanburh.aspx

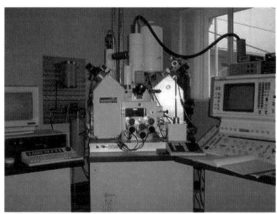

Courtesy of Chris Salter and Alison Crossley, Oxford Materials Characterisation Service (OMCS)

Figure 5. Equipment used to detect the composition of metal objects: Electron Probe Microarray Analysis coupled to Wavelength Dispersive Spectroscopy (EPMA-WDS). High energy electrons in a vacuum are fired at the surface of the object (coin, ingot etc) and from the characteristic intensities and wavelengths of the x-ray spectra emitted the compostion of the element can be identified.
Below left: composition for the Neston coin of Fig. 4 showing silver, Ag (92.9%) and copper, Cu (6.7%) and little else. The coin is "too pure" to be anything older than the 19th century. Below right: composition of a 9th century coin of King Aethelwulf with less silver and the expected presence of significant amounts of other elements such as zinc (Zn), lead (Pb) and cadmium (Cd).

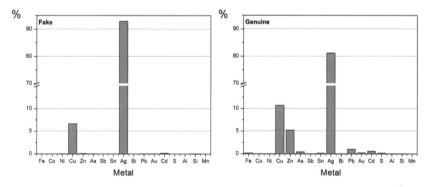

Data courtesy of Rory Naismith (Kings College London) and Peter Northover (OMCS)

This suggestion appeared as a paper later that year[7] with Paul and Professor Judith Jesch, Professor of Viking Studies at the University of Nottingham. So, for a coin to appear at Bromborough's doorstep with Olaf's name on it was deemed a great find, and almost too good to be true ... and so it proved to be. After its discovery in 2007 the coin was duly reported, and registered by the numismatic coin experts at Fitzwilliam Museum at Cambridge as genuine... until a similar coin was discovered being offered for sale on eBay! Suspicions led expert metallurgist, Dr. Peter Northover, at the Oxford Materials Characterisation Service, to perform a test in 2010. This test, known as *Electron Probe Microarray Analysis* (EPMA) coupled to *Wavelength Dispersive Spectroscopy* (WDS), enabled him to check the content of the coin (**Fig. 5**). High energy electrons are fired at the metal and the spectrum of x rays which are given off are recorded. The spectral profile is characteristic of the elements present, and the Neston coin was found to be sterling silver – ~90% silver with some copper. This dated the coin as no earlier than the 19th century: a coin from the Viking Age would have much higher levels of impurity, including lead, zinc and cadmium, such as a coin attributed to the Wessex King Aethelwulf, analysed in the same batch by Peter. It was a brilliant fake that the unsuspecting metal detector enthusiast had found: now it is a matter of course that important finds are checked by EPMA-WDS, which is not too costly to do.

Geophysics and Ground Penetrating Radar

Metal detectors are perhaps the simplest and commonest example of "Geophysics" tools – physical equipment used for probing beneath the surface, whilst leaving any buried artefacts below structurally intact. More complex and powerful geophysical equipment – collectively called "Geophys" by TV's erstwhile *Time Team* – include Magnetometers and Ground Penetrating Radar - and there have been some exciting discoveries by both, either used individually - or in combination with each other. *Magnetometers* work on the principle of detecting magnetized objects under the ground. Different materials below the ground have different *magnetic permeabilities* – a measure of their ability to magnetize. It is not just metals, in fact most materials are at least weakly magnetizable, and magnetometers can detect soils and clays in the substructure under the surface. Magnetometers can also detect the presence of objects or artefacts that can disturb this surface substructure. Scanning in a systematic or grid-like way maximizes the chances of buried objects being detected. *Ground Penetrating Radar (GPR)* is another scanning technique. Instead however of mapping the magnetic properties of the substructure underneath the ground, GPR

---

[7] Cavill P, Harding S, Jesch J (2004) Revisiting Dingesmere. *Journal of the English Place-Name Society*, volume 36, p25-38 www.nottingham.ac.uk/ncmh/harding_pdfs/Paper280.pdf

measures the electrical or *dielectric* properties of the substructure. An electromagnetic pulse of the appropriate wavelength (usually in the microwave region) and intensity is directed into the ground by a portable transmitter. The surface substructure and any objects within it will reflect the radiation back differentially, that is to say in different ways back to a receiver. The time it takes to receive the reflection back from an object to the detector is a measure of the depth, and the intensity and quality of the signal will be a function of the electrical properties or *dielectric constant* of the material. Other related "Geophys" equipment include surface penetrating electrical resistance meters, and *Lidar* (which stands for "Light Radar"). Lidar involves illuminating a particular area of ground with light from a source (often a laser) transmitted from a considerable height (e.g., from a helicopter). Systematic scanning probes characteristic surface features which may reveal topography of archaeological interest otherwise hidden by vegetation. All these "Geophys" probes have revealed exciting finds from the Viking Age. For example magnetometry has been successfully used to reveal the former existence of Viking Age fortresses around the former Viking settlements at Hedeby and Füsing (regarded as the site of the lost Viking town of Sliasthorp) in Schleswig-Holstein and also sunken buildings at Ribe in Jutland[8] . In 2016 a team of geophysicists and archaeologists from Sweden and Germany used GPR to show the existence of a former 30 metre long Viking Age manor near Birka in Sweden[9]. An integrated geophysical approach – including magnetometry and GPR together with other analyses – has been applied to the study of a Viking-age port and settlement at Stavnsager in Jutland[10] as well as to another Viking Age fortress at Aggersborg, Denmark[11].

Now let us take four chaps outside a pub, as shown in the photograph (**Fig. 6**). We're back in Wirral again and for this part of the presentation we focus on the Railway Inn, Meols (an Old Norse name meaning sandhills). For much of the 9th and 10th centuries the Vikings controlled the Irish Sea and Meols or *Melar* was one of its main seaports. In 2007 a planning application was made to construct a patio extension. The assessment that routinely follows in these situations by the County Archaeology Office revealed a document reporting a vessel of unknown

[8] Feveile C, Frandsen LB and Stoumann I (2006) *Mark og Montre*, volume 42, pages 5-11; Hilberg V (2007) http://prusaspira.org/pogezana/Hilberg.pdf; Owen J (2012) – reporting on the work of Anders Domat: http://news.nationalgeographic.com/news/2012/07/120711-lost-viking-town-germany-archaeology-science/
[9] Kalmring S, Runer J, Viberg A (2017) *Archäologisches Korrespondenzblatt*, volume 47, article 1
[10] Loveluck C, Salmon Y (2011). *Antiquity,* volume 85, pages 1402-1417
[11] Brown H, Goodchild H, Sindbæk S (2014). *Internet Archaeology*, volume 36. http://dx.doi.org/10.11141/ia.36.2

antiquity that had been buried underneath. Potentially an archaeologists dream: a major find under a pub! In the 1930s, when previous work was being done, workmen had revealed from under the blue clay part of a clinker vessel. A *clinker* has overlapping planks, a style which originated from Scandinavia in the 1st millennium – mastered by the Angles and the Vikings and characteristic of all their shipping – and a style of boatbuilding so successful it has subsequently been used through the ages and is still used today. However the foreman on duty ordered the workmen to put all the clay back in case the work was held up – by archaeologists! This was duly done and the vessel was largely forgotten about. However the appearance of a sketch of the find made by one of the original workmen - whose son John MaCrae is 2nd right in the photograph - sparked speculation as to the nature and date of the vessel. Two questions arose – was this vessel still underneath, and what was it? This led to the hypothesis: could it have derived from the Viking Age settlers or their descendants? This is where it is useful to have a policeman on the team. First left in the photo is local history sleuth PC Tim Baldock and through the police their geophysics expert, Malcolm Weale – 2nd left – was commissioned. He appears to be holding what at first sight is a Bex Bissell carpet shampooer, but it is in fact an integrated Magnetometer & GPR device. With the enthusiastic support of the Railway, litter bins, plant pots and tables were all moved out of the way, and the area in front of the entrance was systematically scanned and then analysed. A computer then converted the signals into a profile of what is underneath the surface. The results (**Fig. 6**) appear to show the outline of one end of a boat/ship-like artefact. Unfortunately it was not possible to extend the scanning because of a street lamp and other non-movable objects that were in the way. And that is precisely where it stopped in 2007. Excavation was – and still is – not an option because of the enormous costs of preservation and display. Sadly, researchers can't just dig up an interesting wooden find without a full preservation strategy in place: underground in the oxygen-free (anaerobic) blue clay – microbial degradation is minimal and the wood is safe. However, a decade on, plans are being discussed to dig down, take some of the wood sample, and get it dated by measuring carbon-14 levels or using dendrochronology (tree-ring dating)[12]: these techniques I will consider later in this presentation. Of course it would be interesting from a Viking perspective if it turns out to be a vessel built before the Battle of Largs, 1263, a date which probably marks the end of the Viking Age in the Irish Sea and British Isles. As scientists we have to keep an open mind: the Meols boat project is a good example of what scientists call hypothesis driven research.

---

[12] As a first stage in this process, in April 2017 new higher resolution scans have been performed with PM Surveys UK (Queensferry) indicating precisely where to sample

Figure 6. "Geophys" team at the Railway Inn, Meols checking out a report from 1938 there was an old clinker (overlapping planks) vessel buried ~ 2 metres under the patio. After careful scanning and analysis evidence of what appears to be part of a boat shaped artefact can be seen from the side-on view. ^{14}C analysis and dendrochronology will reveal its antiquity.

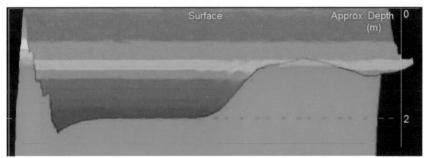

Data courtesy of Malcolm Weale

Figure 7. Above: St. Mary & St. Helen Church at Neston. Conservation team (*courtesy of Neston News*) led by Martin Cooper (2nd right) and Roger White (far right) by a group of stone fragments from at least three Hiberno-Norse crosses. After scanning using a technique known as laser triangulation a replica of one of the crosses has been reconstructed (below) and painted in conjunction with the local community. The cross seems to include the remarkable image of a Viking couple embracing or even dancing.

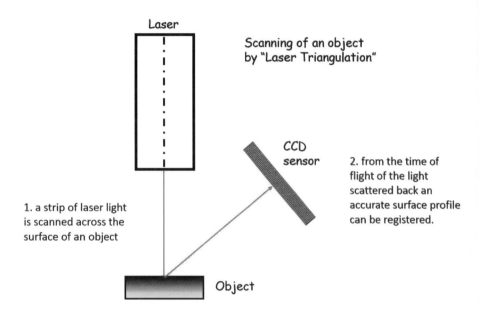

Figure 8. Laser triangulation. Accurate method for scanning objects for the production of replica reconstructions. A strip of laser light is made to scan across the surface of an object and from the time of flight of the light scattered back an accurate surface profile can be registered. The method has been used for example to build a replica reconstruction of one of the Neston crosses (Fig. 7), and is being used to scan artefacts in the Oslo Viking Ship Museum that are under threat of disintegration.

Laser Triangulation and Restoration: the "Viking Lady" Cross

Now let us take another group of chaps (**Fig. 7**), this time in a church, and again in 2007. Inside the Church of St. Mary and St. Helen in Neston there is a collection of remarkable stone fragments which once formed parts of at least three Hiberno-Norse crosses which had been broken up, possibly during the Reformation or the Cromwell periods. The fragments had created a great deal of local interest, particularly from parishioners of St. Mary and St. Helen, with church manager Dr. Peter Rossiter and Rector Neil Robb (far left and 2nd left respectively) in the photograph, and had been extensively studied by archaeologist Dr. Roger White of the University of Birmingham (right). One of the cross fragments shows an animal husbandry or hunting scene and the image of the bottom half of a woman with her arm around the waist of what we presume is her husband. One can also see her hair arranged in a ponytail. Although the rest of the couple's features have been lost, a similar, but complete, female figure – with ponytail – appears also on the Tjängvide stone in Gotland, Sweden, and a similar male figure appears on a cross in Middleton, North Yorkshire.

This facilitated the production of a complete replica cross by the Merseyside Conservation Centre in Liverpool (director Martin Cooper – pictured 2nd right in the photograph), using a technique known as laser triangulation (**Fig. 8**). In this technique a strip of laser light is scanned across the surface of an object and, from the time of flight of the light scattered back, an accurate surface profile can be registered. The laser triangulation name comes from the fact that the laser light source, the object and the detector form the corners of a triangle. This was done for the bottom cross fragment and the ring-headed top part of the cross. The equipment was then taken to Gotland and Yorkshire to scan the hypothetical missing Tjängvide and Middleton parts, and then the whole object was pieced together using a computer which facilitated the production of an exact replica. The Neston cross reconstruction was a great success in public engagement in Science and History, with youngsters from local schools, supervised by Liz Royles, Curator of the Grosvenor Museum in Chester, involved in the painting of the replica cross. The final result was very appealing, and all the stone fragments and the replica are now on display for the local community and visitors to admire.

Similar scanning methodology has been used to restore the Viking Hogback tombstone or memorial – also on display for members of the public – at St. Bridget's Church, West Kirby. It is also being used to scan all the artefacts found with the Oseberg Viking ship – on display at the Vikingskipshuset (Viking Ship Museum) in Oslo, Norway – as a safeguard against future preservation problems. These problems – and how they are being dealt with – will be considered in the next part of my presentation.

IV.   CHEMISTRY AND THE VIKINGS

Isotope Analysis: the Doncaster, Weymouth and Oxford discoveries

In terms of isotopes, for example, ^{16}O and ^{18}O – or "Oxygen 16" and "Oxygen 18" respectively, are different common isotopes of oxygen, that is they contain the same number of protons (8) but different numbers of neutrons (8 and 10): the numbers 16 and 18 refer to the total numbers of protons (which contain a positive charge) and neutrons (which contain no charge) in the atomic nucleus. They are both *stable* isotopes – they are not radioactive or dangerous: they don't decay to emit any radiation for example - but the ratios of the two isotopes $^{18}O/^{16}O$ depends on where on the Earth's globe materials containing oxygen have originally come from – including the remains of people and other life forms when they were alive.

The same applies to other elements like carbon and strontium, where the ratio of their stable isotopes $^{13}C/^{12}C$ (Carbon 13 to Carbon 12) and $^{87}Sr/^{86}Sr$ (Strontium 87 to Strontium 86) also depend on origins. These ratios can be measured by a technique known as *mass spectroscopy*, which measures the mass value (for example this will be either 86 or 87 for Strontium) and amount of each isotope present.

So if we make an archaeological find, we can get an idea from stable isotope analysis of where the find originally came from. For example the ancient remains of a woman were discovered in 2001 at Adwick-le-Street near Doncaster in Yorkshire: from the ratio of the isotopes scientists were able to make some conclusions as to from where she may have originated. Indeed, from the position, depth and objects found with her, it was considered that she may have been Scandinavian in origin. To find this out, researchers performed a mass spectroscopy analysis to determine the isotope ratios of material extracted from the enamel or dentine in her teeth: they were able to show that the isotope levels actually fitted somebody from Scandinavia or from the northeast of Scotland, so it is very possible this woman came from Scandinavia, or had spent part of her life in Scandinavia[13].

A similar approach was also successfully applied to the identification of groups of men buried in Oxford and Weymouth, and, using this technology of measuring the isotope ratios for oxygen and strontium, scientists could show that people within these two groups came from different parts of Scandinavia rather than from one particular place. Furthermore, by measuring the protein or

---

[13] Speed G, Rogers PW (2004) A burial of a Viking woman at Adwick-le-Street, South Yorkshire. *Medieval Archaeology*, volume 48, pages 51-90

collagen in the bone for Carbon 14 (^{14}C) levels, the remains could be dated. Carbon 14 is an unstable or *radioactive* isotope of carbon: it decays to yield the normal isotope of nitrogen (^{14}N – Nitrogen 14), a beta ray (an electron) and gamma (γ) radiation according to the decay equation

$$^{14}C \rightarrow {^{14}N} + \beta^- + \gamma$$

Carbon 14 has a "half life" (i.e. the time it takes for the radioactivity to decay by a half) of 5730 years (this means it takes another 5730 years to reduce by half again, then another 5730 years to decay a further half, and so on..). Essentially, when the living object/person dies, it stops incorporating new carbon (including ^{14}C), and the rate at which radioactivity is emitted by the object/person – and the levels of ^{14}C in that object/person – will gradually reduce with time.

So by measuring the ^{14}C levels in a substance using mass spectroscopy (a technique we have just discussed in relation to stable isotope studies) or using specialized counters called Geiger or scintillation counters for measuring the radioactivity levels, scientists can date the former living object or person to a reasonable degree of precision. For example, using this technology, the warriors found at Weymouth were shown, from analysis of the carbon containing protein (collagen) in the bone, to come from the period AD930 - 1000, consistent with them being Viking Age people.

Researchers have also used this technology, in conjunction with *dendrochronology* (studying the growth rings in the wood), to help date the Viking ships that have been found in Scandinavia: for example the Skuldelev series of ships beautifully displayed at Roskilde, Denmark, the Askekärr ship at Gothenburg, Sweden, and perhaps, most famously, the ships and associated artefacts found with them around Oslofjorden (the Oslo Fjord), now displayed at the Viking Skiphuset (Ship Museum) at Bygdøy, Oslo.

Polymer Chemistry: Saving the Oseberg Project

As soon as you enter the Skiphuset in Oslo you are confronted with the magnificent Oseberg ship directly in front of you (**Fig. 9**), with two further Viking ships – the Gokstad to the left and the Tune ship to the right – together with some smaller boats or *faerings*. The Oseberg was a burial ship and, when it was excavated in 1904, found on board were the remains of two women, together with an array of wonderful artefacts, including a wagon, sledges, buckets, barrels and beds (**Fig. 10**). The remains of the women were, through respect, rightfully re-buried under the ground. The objects were preserved and put on display for Norwegians and others to learn about their history and heritage.

Figure 9. The Oseberg – one of three major Viking Ship discoveries now preserved and displayed at the Viking Ship Museum in Oslo. Artefacts discovered with the ship and displayed at back of the hall, are now in danger of disintegration. Below, conservator Paul Johannessen, soon after the excavation in 1904, reassembling objects treated with hot (90°C) alum to prevent the waterlogged wood from shrinking on drying. Long-term degradation of wood by sulphuric acid arising from this treatment has now become a critical problem. *Courtesy of the Cultural History Museum, University of Oslo*

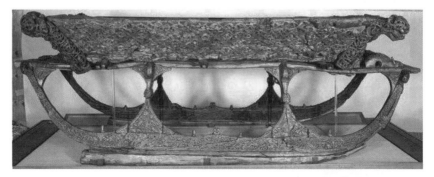

Figure 10. Some of the Oseberg artefacts under serious threat of alum induced disintegration.

Photographs courtesy of the Cultural History Museum, University of Oslo

Photographs courtesy of the Cultural History Museum, University of Oslo

Figure 11. Top: The newly constructed Saving Oseberg research laboratories located behind the Viking Ship Museum. Middle: the state of a piece of alum treated wood (viewed by x-ray tomographic microscopy, XTM) and a high resolution scanning electron microscopy (SEM) image: high energy electrons behave like waves and can be focussed to produce a high magnification image. 1 μm = a thousandth of a millimetre (mm). The pores in the wood and crystals of alum (arrowed) are seen. Below: chitin from the shells of crabs and lobsters can be treated to give cellulose-like chitosan which can potentially replace cellulose and take out acid (hydrogen ions). Lower right: image of a chitosan molecule obtained by atomic force microscopy (AFM), which gives even higher resolution than SEM. 1 nanometre (nm) is a millionth of a mm.

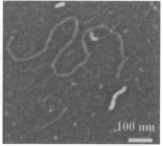

However, following serious decay of the wood fibre, the objects are protected behind glass screens since they are now so fragile. Why? After the excavation of the Oseberg and its artefacts from the waterlogged blue clay surrounding Oslo Fjord, (an ideal preservative[14]), the first task for the conservators was to stop the wood from shrinking when it dried: this would cause serious mis-shaping and destroy all the intricate patterns that had been painstakingly carved in the wood by Viking craftsmen. What they used was a material called alum – potassium aluminium sulphate dodecahydrate to be precise:

$$K.Al.(SO_4)_2.12H_2O$$

Maybe some of you, like me, remember growing crystals of alum in Chemistry class at school? And this is precisely what Paul Johannessen, the Conservator, did in 1904: he first treated the wood from the artefacts with hot alum, which, on cooling, crystallizes inside the wood, reinforces the wood fibre, and successfully stops shrinkage when the wood dries out, thus retaining its shape.... and with minimal distortion to the carvings. However, what Paul and his colleagues perhaps had not foreseen was that the treatment with alum at high temperature (90°C) resulted in an unwanted side-effect: the generation of significant levels of sulphuric acid H_2SO_4, which is not good! Over the course of the last 110 years or so, this has gradually decayed away almost all the wood fibre (cellulose and lignin), with the result that these objects – Norway's national treasure and symbol of national independence – are now under immediate threat of being lost. All that is seemingly holding many of the objects together at the moment are the surface coatings – external lacquer and varnish – and remaining alum crystals still present inside the wood.

It is worth stressing that the Oseberg ship and the other ships (Gokstad, Tune) are themselves not under immediate risk as they were never treated with alum. In the future, once the artefacts have been dealt with, some sort of long-term preservation strategy for these will, however, also be necessary. At this particular moment in time, saving the artefacts is of the utmost priority. And so 2015 saw the first meeting of the Saving Oseberg Research Group, with the Saving Oseberg laboratories being built and equipped shortly afterwards, just behind the ship museum (**Fig. 11**). The Norwegian government have provided a generous grant for the team of scientists from Norway, UK, Germany, Sweden, Denmark and Italy, to try and get this right.

Behind the surface coatings is rotten wood, and the problem is illustrated beautifully by the x-ray tomographic microscopy (XTM) image. The image has

---

[14] Waterlogged blue clay is "anaerobic" – lacking oxygen – meaning microorganisms that produce chemicals which attack the wood cannot thrive

been generated by measuring the intensity shadow left after absorption of x-rays penetrating through the wood. The lighter areas in the wood are the alum salts. It is possible to see what is going on in a wood sample at a much higher magnification using a technique known as *Scanning Electron Microscopy (SEM)* (**Fig. 11**). Here we use high energy electrons which behave as waves - like light waves but at much smaller wavelengths - so you can produce an image of an object (in this case the Oseberg wood) on a scale of microns (a 1000th of a millimetre). You can clearly see the pores inside the wood fibre: virtually all the cellulose has gone. A substantial part of the lignin still remains but has been degraded. The rather beautiful looking alum crystals – which still help preserve the structure – are still clearly present. So, we have to replace the cellulose and lignin with acid-resistant natural polymers or '*consolidants*' that will give the wood its strength back – and reduce the acid. And we have to do this somehow without disturbing the remaining wood and its intricate carvings.

This is the task of the research group, and amazingly Norway may have its own natural resource to solve the problem, a resource which is a bi-product of its seafood industry. Norway has lots of coastline because of all the fjords, and hence lots of crabs and lobsters. The shells of these crustaceans contain chitin which gives the crab and lobster their firm external structure. The chitin structure stops the crab from falling apart, keeps the inside of the crab from dehydrating, and prevents external water from getting in. The chitin can be modified by the addition of strong alkali to give a new substance called chitosan[15]:

The above structure represents the repeat unit in the chitosan polymer. R can be an acetyl group –OCH_3 or a hydrogen, –H, the proportion of which depends on the extent of treatment by alkali. The repeat number n can be between 5 and 50, depending on processing conditions. The important point is that the structure for chitosan above is just like cellulose, except it has groups on it called amino groups

---

[15] Harding SE, Tombs MP, Adams GG, Paulsen BS, Inngjerdingen, KT, Barsett H (2017) *An Introduction to Polysaccharide Biotechnology*, 2nd edition, CRC Press, Boca Raton, USA; Harding SE, editor (2012) *Stability of Complex Carbohydrate Structures : Biofuels, Foods, Vaccines and Shipwrecks*, Royal Society of Chemistry, Cambridge

$-NH_2$ which can neutralize out acid (hydrogen ions H^+): $-NH_2 + H^+ = -NH_3^+$. For this reason we are focusing on these and related molecules known as *aminocelluloses* as potential wood consolidants to replace the cellulose. Similar progress is being made in replacing the lignins with similar materials called *isoeugenols*, slightly modified to make them more resistant to degradation[16]. It is an exciting problem in carbohydrate chemistry, and fortunately there is a sufficient supply of old wood found alongside the Oseberg which is ideal for testing these ideas out.

V. BIOLOGY AND THE VIKINGS

No presentation on *Science and the Vikings* would be complete without reference to DNA, and what it is telling us about the origins of populations of people. This includes research we have been doing since 2003 with scientists from the Department of Genetics at the University of Leicester. Leicester University is the birthplace of Forensic Genetics, following Sir Alec Jeffreys' ground breaking work on DNA fingerprinting, featured in the two-part ITV documentary *Code of a Killer*, broadcast in April 2015.

Our research – with Professor Mark Jobling and Dr. Turi King – has been looking for Viking ancestry of populations of people in northern England. The first part (which ran from 2003 to 2008) covered Wirral and West Lancashire. The second part started in 2010 and is covering North Lancashire, Cumbria and Yorkshire. For the Wirral and West Lancashire study Turi was then a PhD student. She has subsequently become world famous for her work on Richard III. Although, as I am sure you are aware, there have been several studies on various aspects of DNA and Vikings, our research has been different as it has focussed on populations of people using *surnames* as a guide to volunteer recruitment in order to circumvent the problem of large population movements in the British Isles since the Industrial Revolution. DNA (**Fig. 12**) of course forms our genes which code for what we are – eye colour, hair colour, height, whether we are male or female and so on. It also contains messages from the past because our DNA has been passed down to us from our ancestors, and so if we can analyse our DNA

---

[16] McHale E, Braovac S, Steindal CC, Gillis RB, Adams GG, Harding SE, Benneche T, Kutzke H (2016) Synthesis and characterisation of lignin-like oligomers as a bio-inspired consolidant for waterlogged archaeological wood. *Pure and Applied Chemistry*, DOI: 10.1515/pac-2016-0814; McHale E, Steindal CC, Kutzke H, Benneche T, Harding SE (2017) In situ polymerisation of isoeugenol as a green consolidation method for waterlogged archaeological wood. *Scientific Reports (Nature)* SREP-16-46481

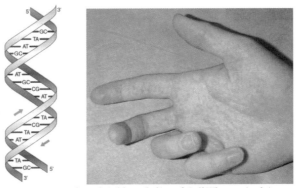

Courtesy of Mark Jobling (left) and Jeff Whiting (right)

Figure 12. Top: DNA and a genetic trait associated with Scandinavian ancestry – Dupuytren's contracture. Bottom: DNA testing of uniparentally inherited markers (mitochondrial DNA and Y chromosomal DNA) can provide information about one line of ancestry for women and two lines for men. Paternally inherited Y chromosomal DNA can be linked with paternally inherited surnames.

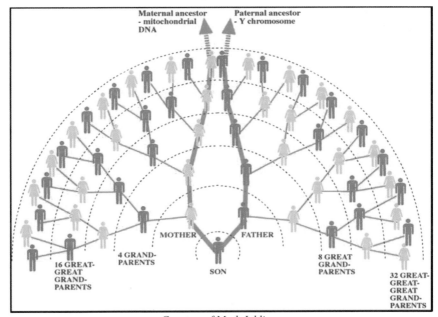

Courtesy of Mark Jobling

27

in an appropriate way we can potentially find out about our past and where we might have come from, either as individuals or as populations.

External manifestations of genes: "Phenotypes"

Until the development of genetic tools, genetic analysis had been limited to the study of the distribution of external manifestations of genes. These are referred to as "phenotype" characteristics. Blood groups are genetically determined but unfortunately for ancestral studies are poorly discriminating and widespread in many populations, and are regarded as not sensitive enough to be used as markers for ancestry. Other such characteristics are skin pigmentation, stature and facial shape with oval faces supposedly representing people of Scandinavian origin[17]. These features are however complex, poorly understood and widely distributed across northern Europe. Eye-colour and hair-colour have also been considered as distinctive markers. The highest proportions of people with fair hair and blue eyes appear to be found in central Sweden, Norway, Finland, the Baltic States, the northern parts of Poland and the former German Democratic Republic with a reported 70 to 80% possessing these phenotypes[18]. However the genetic basis behind these is not completely understood and in any case it is difficult to tag these to Viking migrations into the British Isles as these particular genetic traits could have been brought here before the Viking Age – from the Angles, for example, who originate from Southern Scandinavia and Northern Germany.

Particular physical impairments or diseases that are more prevalent in Scandinavia could be said to track the distribution of Scandinavian genetic influence. One such condition which has been considered to have derived from Scandinavia is *Dupuytren's contracture*. This is a condition of the hand that some people can get in their 50s and 60s. It involves a tightening of the elastic tissue in the palm, preventing the flexing of the 4th and 5th fingers and can be treated by a surgical operation. It is a condition common in Scandinavia and in places colonised by the Vikings. A recent Mayor of Wirral for example had the condition in both hands. Famous people to have had this condition include Mrs. Margaret Thatcher who hails from Lincolnshire – part of the old Danelaw and once heavily settled by the Vikings. The genetics behind the condition however is not properly understood, and, as with all the other physical characteristics, it is not a robust measure of Viking ancestry[19].

---

[17] Geipel J (1969) *The Europeans: An Ethnohistorical Survey*. Longman, London

[18] Beals RL & Hoijer H (1965) *An Introduction to Anthropology* (3rd edition). Macmillan, New York; Frost P (1976) *Evolution and Human Behaviour*, volume 27, pages 85-103

[19] Jobling M (2011) The Baron's complaint. *Investigative Genetics*, volume 2, article 18

Analysis of DNA – the Y-chromosome and its link with paternal surnames

A more rigorous approach is to analyse the DNA directly, and this has become possible with the great advances in molecular genetics following Professor Jeffreys' revolutionary DNA fingerprinting work at the University of Leicester in the 1980s. The DNA we have inherited from our ancestors is mostly packaged into chromosomes, and we have 23 pairs of these, 22 "autosomes" and 1 pair of sex chromosomes: females have two "X" chromosomes, males have one X and one shorter chromosome called the Y chromosome. An individual's DNA comes from his/her mother and father, and each chromosome contains half from each which is mixed or recombined apart from the Y-chromosome in men which is passed down the paternal line – father to son to his son etc. with little or no change. So a man will contain the same DNA on the Y-chromosome as his paternal ancestor back to the Viking Age and beyond, apart from some possible mutations on parts of the huge DNA chain (or pair of chains).

In particular one of the 4 bases, adenine (A), thymine (T), cytosine (C), guanine (G), at a particular location along the Y-chromosome, could mutate, during the course of time, to one of the others. This mutation is called a single nucleotide polymorphism, or "SNP". The sequence of bases at particular locations on the Y-chromosome defines a man's Y-DNA type or *haplogroup*, and these haplogroups occur at different frequencies in different parts of the world. For example a haplogroup that might have its origins in ancient Germany is T1a1, from the recent remarkable find from the bones of two unrelated individuals several thousand years old at Karsdorf[20]. T1a1 is part of a larger group of haplogroups or "superhaplogroup" known as K. Another haplogroup which appears to be particularly common in Norway, and in regions settled by the Norwegian Vikings, is known as R1a1, and this has been used as a marker for Scandinavian ancestry.

There is also another part of our DNA which is passed down from our ancestors with little or no change: this is mitochondrial DNA, which is passed down the maternal line (from mother to her son and daughter – but only the daughter can pass it down to her children and so on): and there are corresponding maternal haplogroups – such as H1, commonly found in Scandinavia.

---

[20] Haak W, Lazaridis I, Patterson N, Rohland N, Mallick S, Llamas B, Brandt G, Nordenfelt S, Harney E, Stewardson K, Fu Q, Mittnik A, Bánffy E, Economou C, Francken M, Friederich S, Garrido Pena R, Hallgren F, Khartanovich V, Khokhlov A, Kunst M, Kuznetsov P, Meller H, Mochalov O, Moiseyev V, Nicklisch N, Pichler SL, Risch R, Guerra MAR, Roth C, Szécsényi-Nagy A, Wahl J, Meyer M, Krause J, Brown D, Anthony D, Cooper A, Alt KW, Reich M (2015) *Nature*, volume 522, pages 207–211. Remarkably, from analysis of the autosomal DNA, it has been possible to ascertain some features of what the individuals may have looked like – for example they were both likely to have either light grey or blue eyes.

So a man has two direct lines to his past – his paternal line through his Y-chromosome and his maternal line through the mitochondrial DNA bequeathed from his mother. A woman has only one direct line – through her mitochondrial DNA, as she does not have a Y-chromosome. So, to give an example, in our Harding family, my four Sons will have my Y-DNA, and my wife's mitochondrial DNA, but my Granddaughter will have neither – but will possess instead the mitochondrial DNA from my Daughter-in law who is from eastern Germany.

It is possible now also to obtain an idea of ancestry from all our other "autosomal" chromosome DNA, and commercial testers, e.g. National Geographic can give members of the public prepared to pay for the test an estimate of which global populations of people they are closest to. An individual ancestral DNA test done through a commercial company (as opposed to a research project, which to a volunteer is generally free) can cost between £100 and £200. It has now become very popular and is creating more and more interest as people seek to find out more about their origins.

DNA testing is however much more powerful when done on a *population* rather than on an *individual* basis. The best way – if it were possible – of assessing Viking ancestry in a region would be to analyse populations of DNA haplogroups from bones and remains of people known from radiocarbon ^{14}C dating to be from the Viking Age in that region and compare them with DNA from the bones of people dated to the Viking Age in Scandinavia. However this is currently impossible in Britain and Ireland because sample sizes of *Ancient DNA* from regions of the British Isles are small or of poor quality and prone to contamination, and there may well be no descendants of such people living today. In the future it may be possible at least to get sufficient numbers of samples from Viking Age human remains in Scandinavia that could provide important control data for any modern based population study. Erika Hagelberg and colleagues have been exploring the possibilities for mitochondrial DNA based on the Schreiner collection at the University of Oslo[21].

Practically, for assessing Viking ancestry in populations from various regions in the British Isles, the Y-chromosome is a useful tool, and it has one very important feature: it is not only the Y-DNA which is passed down the paternal line but also a man's *surname*. As we have said above, this link between surnames and Y-DNA is particularly important when studying the ancestry of urbanised

---

[21] Krzewinska M, Bjørnstad G, Skoglund P, Olason PI, Bill J, Götherström A, Hagelberg E (2015) Mitochondrial DNA variation in the Viking Age population of Norway. *Philosophical Transactions of the Royal Society*, volume B 370, article 20130384

areas, which have undergone a huge change in population since the Industrial Revolution. By focusing the survey on men who possess surnames that were present in the area before the Industrial Revolution, complications caused by modern population movements can be minimized.

Genetic Survey of Northern England, Part I: Wirral and West Lancashire

The link between surnames and the Y-chromosomal DNA formed the basis of the survey of Northern England, which started with the Wirral and West Lancashire Project, and ran from 2003 to 2008. The project was supported by a grant from the United Kingdom Biotechnology and Biological Sciences Research Council (BBSRC) to commemorate the 50th anniversary of the discovery of the DNA Double Helix by Watson and Crick in 1953, and is an example of how interdisciplinary research into the Viking Age has now become. It involved geneticists, biochemists, place name experts, surname experts and local heritage associations, and so, when the final results were published in the Oxford University Press journal *Molecular Biology & Evolution* in 2008, it comprised what seemed to be a football team of authors! **Figure 13** shows this.

Suitable volunteers from both Wirral and West Lancashire had to have their paternal grandfather from either region, and also to possess a surname that was present in the particular area before 1700. In Wirral this included a comprehensive list of names of people paying taxes in Henry VIII's reign (or their modern equivalents), criminal records (e.g. Harding & Poole where accused of killing a dog and damaging hedges in Neston – found not guilty!) and alehouse records. In West Lancashire this included an extensive list of names of people paying towards the stipend of the Priest of the Church of Our Lady at Ormskirk. In addition, Wirral or Lancastrian men who had surnames that were place names in the region (Scarisbrick, Melling, Raby, etc) could also participate.

In the case of duplicate surnames only one was allowed in the calculation of the results (taken at random, although in most cases men of the same surname had identical haplogroups): so these represented as best we could the 'Medieval" or pre-Industrial Revolution populations in the two areas. As a control, "modern" populations from both areas were also sampled with only the paternal grandfather criterion but without the surname criterion. And the results were compared with "British" samples (taken from central Ireland and Scotland), Norway, Orkney, Shetland, Llangefni (Anglesey), Isle of Man, Penrith (Lake District) and Mid-Cheshire.

Excavating Past Population Structures by Surname-Based Sampling: The Genetic Legacy of the Vikings in Northwest England

Georgina R. Bowden,* Patricia Balaresque,* Turi E. King,* Ziff Hansen,† Andrew C. Lee,*[1]
Giles Pergl-Wilson,† Emma Hurley,† Stephen J. Roberts,‡ Patrick Waite,§ Judith Jesch,‖ Abigail
L. Jones,¶ Mark G. Thomas,# Stephen E. Harding,† and Mark A. Jobling*

*Department of Genetics, University of Leicester, Leicester, United Kingdom; †National Centre for Macromolecular Hydrodynamics, University of Nottingham, Sutton Bonington Campus, Loughborough, United Kingdom; ‡The Queen Katherine School, Kendal, Cumbria, United Kingdom; §West Lancashire Heritage Association, Ormskirk, United Kingdom; ‖School of English Studies, University of Nottingham, University Park, Nottingham, United Kingdom; ¶The Centre for Genetic Anthropology, Department of Biology, University College London, London, United Kingdom; and #Department of Biology, University College London, London, United Kingdom

Figure 13. Top: Publication in 2008 in *Molecular Biology and Evolution* (volume 25, pages 301-309) of the results of the Wirral & West Lancashire genetic survey showing the "football team" list of co-authors from different disciplines. Middle: strong ethical rules have to be followed when sampling people's DNA – form filling at Ormskirk at the start of the project. Left: automatic analyser for characterising a man's Y- DNA type, after amplification of his DNA signal by a reaction known as the Polymerase Chain Reaction (PCR).

The test is very simple. It involves swabbing the inside cheek of the mouth (which collects cells and the DNA inside them) using a brush, placing the contents of the swab in a tube containing a detergent preservative – similar to what is used in household washing up liquids, and then the samples are analysed in the lab utilising a technique known as the *Polymerase Chain Reaction* (PCR), which magnifies the relevant parts of the DNA. This is followed by haplogroup identification, a process which is largely automated, so samples can be analysed in multiple batches once the instrumentation has been set up.

Distributions of all the various haplogroups in the different areas were compared using for example the "pie charts" of **Fig. 14**, including for example R1a1 – the light grey sector in the figure. My own group is part of the orange sector – K*(xR1) for 'Medieval' Wirral. K*(xR1) means "the superhaplogroup K excluding the R1 haplogroups".

Statistical *"admixture"* calculations are then performed using computers to assess the proportion of Scandinavian ancestry. Almost 50% was found for both the 'Medieval' West Lancashire and Wirral populations, commensurate with the levels found in modern Orkney and Shetland. If volunteers with 'common' surnames (i.e. with a frequency of more than 10,000 in the UK) were excluded the proportions increased even more.

A similar result is obtained if just the levels of R1a1 in various populations are compared. What is also interesting is how close the distributions are for both Wirral and West Lancashire, showing the Mersey has been no barrier to population movement. The results also tie in beautifully with the high density of Viking place names in both areas – and of course the existence of the two Thingwalls[22] - so perhaps it was not too surprising.

After the 'academic' 2008 paper was published, and following a large number of popular requests, Mark, Turi and I produced a book *Viking DNA, The Wirral and West Lancashire Project*[23], which explains the project and its results in a less technical way, (it also includes in its introduction a photograph of the infamous Olaf Guthfrithsson fake coin!). The book includes a superb foreword by another well-known BBC Presenter Michael Wood. The results had also been presented in November 2007 at a meeting at Knowsley Hall, Liverpool, organized by the West Lancashire Heritage Association. At the end of the presentation, as a matter of curiosity, Mark asked for a show of hands of those people who had Dupuytren's contracture. A noticeably greater than average proportion of the audience raised their crimped hands!

---

[22] See pages 3 and 10
[23] CRC Press, Boca Raton USA (2010)

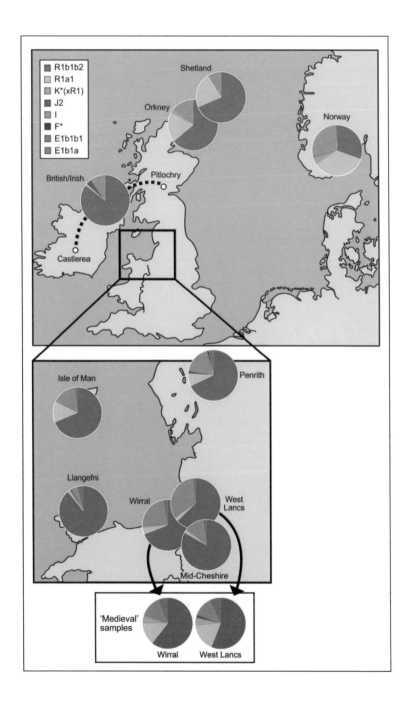

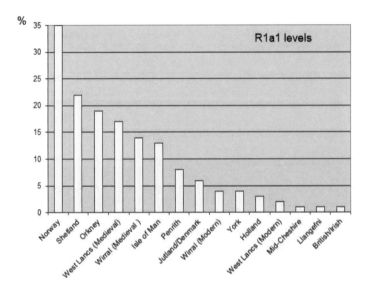

Figure 14. Facing: Results from Part I of the Northern England Viking Ancestry Project (Wirral and West Lancashire). Distribution of Y-DNA haplogroups. The greater the pie slice the greater the proportion of people with that group. "Medieval" samples are the data-sets based on men with surnames present in the area before 1600, crucial for getting behind the large population movements that have occurred since the Industrial Revolution. From computer based statistical comparisons it is possible to estimate the extent of Scandinavian ancestry in areas. A key signature is R1a1, shown in the pie charts facing and also in the histogram above. For Part II the survey has moved up the coast to North Lancashire, Cumbria up to the Solway, and across to Yorkshire and Northumbria.

Genetic Survey of Northern England, Part II: North Lancashire, Cumbria, Yorkshire and Northumbria

The second part of the Northern England survey started in 2010. Turi had now obtained her PhD and so took over the lead from Mark and myself. A large number of men have been sampled – again as with Part I, following strict surname criteria - and their haplogroups determined.

All the analyses and statistical comparisons are due to be completed in the near future. It has taken longer because the resources of the Leicester team had to be directed to the incredible story of the "King under the car park" (another car park!) – i.e. the discovery of the skeleton of a man under a supermarket car park at Leicester. The man under the car park had the same backbone condition – Scoliosis – as Richard III was known to have had. Historians and archaeologists knew he was buried in Leicester - somewhere. Mitochondrial DNA analysis conducted by Turi, from the bones of the man, showed it was the same (rare) type as a Canadian man who could trace his maternal line back to Margaret, Richard III's sister, confirming this was indeed the missing King of Shakespearian/ Sir Laurence Olivier fame. This was one of the most exciting finds of DNA ancestry research.

Once the Part II study is completed, I am sure you will agree with me that there is a good argument for a Part III, continuing along the Western coast of Scotland at least as far as Largs: these are areas like my own Wirral, steeped in Norwegian Viking tradition. It would follow the same criteria of volunteer recruitment, i.e. men possessing surnames that were present in the area before 1700. I will discuss this with Turi and Mark!

There is also a case for extending the survey to the East Midlands "English Danelaw". The difficulty here is that the Danish Vikings came from the same part of the world as the Anglo Saxons: Jutland is part of Denmark and so was Angeln until the 19th Century, and the major Y-chromosome haplogroup distributions will be virtually the same. The methodology, however, is becoming more and more resolving as new sub-haplogroups within the major haplogroups are continually being discovered; so there *may* also be a case for an East Midlands study in the future.

Since the start of the Part II study, we have also been working with local historical societies in Norway to see if there is any regional variation in the 'Medieval' populations of Norway, and to get better control data from the Western fjord areas, where the Norwegian Vikings coming to the British Isles are most likely to have come from.

Figure 15. In 2010 Turi, Mark and myself met up with Norwegian historians Sigurd
Aase and Harald Løvvik who assisted in the recruitment of volunteers for control data
for the Part II survey and as part of a separate study on Old Norway. Above: we were
also shown by Harald (left) Sigurd's huge (35m long) modern construction of a ship –
the Draken Harald Hårfagre – built on Viking tradition. On completion in May 2013
a postage stamp appeared in its honour

Figure 16. June 2013: Simple biological experiment appears to show Vikings may not have been as tall as we thought! Sigurd invited me to bring a Viking Navy of trained enthusiasts from NW England and the East Midlands to row the Draken Harald Hårfagre as part of the Karmøy Viking Festival. The ship – with oar spacing based on the Oseberg and Gokstad ships – can take 50 pairs of oarsmen, 2 to an oar or rowed singly. The rowing technique was a bit disastrous at first, but after changing from full to ¾ strokes the rhythm became much smoother. An unwitting but simple experiment which perhaps shows either that the rowing style in the Viking Age may have been quite different from todays style – or oarsman were shorter! All this took place in view of Olavskirken - the Church of St. Olav at Avaldsnes founded by… Hakon Hakonsson.

Courtesy of Anita Langåker Arnøy

The study in Norway includes an investigation on the regional variation of subgroups within the haplogroup R1a1, and a publication from that research is due shortly, headed by Mark's team. Two of the key people who have been helping us are historians and Viking enthusiasts, Harald Løvikk and Sigurd Aase, both based at Haugesund. Sigurd has also been patron of an ambitious project involving the construction of a modern age vessel built in the Viking ship tradition (**Fig. 15**).

Postscript: A simple biological experiment which suggests that Viking blokes may have been shorter!

Based on the Oseberg and Gokstad ships at the Oslo Vikingskipshuset/ Viking Ship Museum, Sigurd's vessel even includes such details as the distance between the oars. The ship has however been made much larger to correspond with one of the *leiðangr* series of vessels that once patrolled the Western fjords in the latter part of the Viking Age, probably including the time of the Battle of Largs[24].

Mark, Turi and myself visited the early parts of its construction at nearby Avaldsnes, Karmøy, in June 2010, and, by May 2013, this huge 35 metre long vessel – named the *Draken Harald Hårfagre* – had been constructed, with 50 pairs of oars, two people to each oar. The name was very appropriately chosen since Harald Hårfagre was one of the most famous of Norway's Viking kings, responsible for uniting the kingdoms into one country. Harald Hårfagre also had his Royal residence at Avaldsnes.

Following Sigurd's invitation – and with the help of Liverpool Victoria Rowing Club, Loughborough Boat Club and Nottingham Boat Club, who provided the training – I took a Viking 'Navy' of over 50 volunteers from Wirral, West Lancashire and the East Midlands to row the ship as part of the Karmøy Viking Festival (**Fig. 16**). The 'Navy' included PAS/Portable Antiquities Scheme Finds Liaison Officer Wendy Scott, and Viking novelist Giles Christian. Sigurd paid for our 'Viking style' hostel accommodation and for over two days we rowed the beautiful vessel in perfect rowing conditions in the Avaldsnes fjord.

At first, despite our training, the rowing and timing was very ragged, with everyone crashing into the rower in front. However, if we took ¾ strokes it was fine. The conclusion obtained from this very basic, but nonetheless very relevant,

---

[24] Professor Judith Jesch has recently considered in detail what scholars consider the end of the Viking Age, and provides a reasoned argument for a 'long Viking Age'. Jesch J (2015) *The Viking Diaspora*, Routledge, London & New York, Chapter 3.

biological experiment was as follows: either the rowing style was different in the Viking Age… or the average Viking bloke was shorter than the average bloke today!

Most appropriately, all this activity took place in full view of *Olavskirken* - the Church of St. Olav at Avaldsnes, a Church that was founded by none other than … Hakon Hakonsson. If he and Magnus Magnusson were still with us today, I hope they would have both approved!

Finally it remains for me to thank Lord Glasgow, Irene Innes and fellow colleagues at the Largs Historical Society for being excellent hosts for this evening. I would like to thank also staff at the Valhalladrome for this superb auditorium, and of course to you all for being an excellent audience.

If anyone would like to see or hear the lecture again it has been recorded[25] – and if anyone has any specific questions or comments after this evening then I will be absolutely delighted to hear from you. I can be reached on the following address: steve.harding@nottingham.ac.uk

Thank you.

---

[25] https://www.youtube.com/watch?v=HOKcv-G3LqM&feature=youtu.be

Appendix: Short glossary of some of the key terms used in scientific research on the Viking Age

AFM: atomic force microscopy. Technique used to scan an object at very high magnification. A detector tip on a cantilever traces across an object and profiles across the surface. The height of the cantilever as it profiles across the object is using a laser, producing an image.

Anaerobic. Oxygen depleted environment. Most microbes that degrade wood are aerobic – need oxygen –so an anaerobic environment is best for wood.

Birefringence. Splitting of light into two beams by special crystals such as Iceland Spar (calcite), thus causing the formation of two images of an object.

Cellulose: A carbohydrate polymer which is a major constituent of wood. Forms fibres which gives the wood its strength.

Chitin. Tough, watertight and large carbohydrate polymer material – similar to cellulose – which forms the shells of crabs and lobsters.

Chitosan. Chitin treated with strong alkali to give a large carbohydrate polymer with positive charges.

Consolidant. A material used to replace/ support degraded wood.

Dendrochronology. Study of the age of trees or wood from the numbers of growth rings (one ring or layer corresponds to one year).

DNA. Deoxyribonucleic acid. Large, double stranded molecule which contains the genetic code.

DNA, mitochondrial. Most of our DNA is in the form of long chains on chromosomes (we have 23 pairs). A small part of our DNA is circular and in mitochondria. Most chromosomal DNA in an individual is a mix from DNA bequeathed from his/her mother and his/her father. Mitochondrial DNA comes only from his/her mother, so is passed along the maternal line unchanged unless there is a (very rare) mutation.

DNA, Y-chromosomal. We have 23 pairs of chromosomes, including one pair of sex chromosomes. Women have a similar pair of sex chromosomes, known as X chromosomes. Men have just one X, paired with a shorter chromosome known as Y. The DNA on the Y chromosome is different from all other chromosomal DNA in that it is passed along the paternal line with no change – unless there is a (very rare) mutation.

Dupuytren's contracture. Genetic condition of the hand: tightening of elastic tissue limiting flexing of the 4th and 5th fingers, a condition which has been considered to have originated in Scandinavia.

Eddy current. Electrical current in an object induced by a magnetic field, e.g. generated by a metal detector.

EPMA. Electron probe micro-array analysis. Technique used to find the composition of a metal object. A high energy electron beam is fired at the metal and x-rays are given off, characteristic of particular element (silver, iron etc.). Used to ascertain the antiquity of a metal object.

GPR: ground penetrating radar. Radar waves which can penetrate underneath the surface to a depth of several meters. The time it takes to be reflected back and the quality of signal help us map underneath a surface without having to dig.

Half-life. Time for radioactivity from an object – e.g. ^{14}C radioactivity – to decay to half of its original value. It will take the same time to decrease by half of this again, and so on.

Haplogroup. DNA group of an individual (either Y-chromosome DNA – men, or mitochondrial DNA – men and women).

Isotope. Many elements have slightly different masses. e.g. Carbon can have a mass of 12 units (the most common form, abbreviated as ^{12}C) or 13 or 14. These are known as isotopes of the same element.

Isotope, Radioactive. An isotope which is unstable (emits radioactivity and decays to a more stable isotope). Carbon 14, ^{14}C (unstable) decays to the stable form of Nitrogen 14, ^{14}N emitting radioactivity.

Isotope, Stable. An isotope that does not emit radioactivity, e.g. ^{12}C, ^{13}C, ^{14}N.

Laser triangulation. Used to scan accurately the surface of an object. The time it takes for a laser beam to be reflected from a particular point in the object to a detector depends on the distance the light has to travel. The laser source, object and detector form the corners of a triangle, hence "triangulation". Powerful tool in restoration technology.

Lignin. Sheet like polymers found in natural materials such as wood. In wood they form complexes with the main wood component, cellulose, and are more resistant to degradation.

Magnetometry. A variety of materials in the substructure under the ground can be weakly magnetized caused by the earth's magnetic field. A magnetometer detects and delineates between these different magnetizations and also can detect the presence of embedded objects which disturb this substructure.

Phenotype: Physical characteristics deriving from a gene or group of genes – such as Dupuytren's contracture.

PCR: polymerase chain reaction. A laboratory technique used to amplify the amount of part of the DNA on a chromosome or in a mitochondrion, so that it can be analysed to determine the paternal or maternal haplogroup.

SEM: scanning electron microscopy. Very high magnification microscopy using electron rather than light waves to scan an object and produce an image. Conducted under vacuum conditions to prevent absorption (loss) of the electrons.

XTM: x-ray tomographic microscopy. Lower magnification microscopy using x-rays which pass through an object and are "attenuated" or absorbed to different amounts depending on the density profile of the interior. A good, non-destructive probe for visualizing the interiors of wooden structures.

Also by the author (both books by CRC Press):

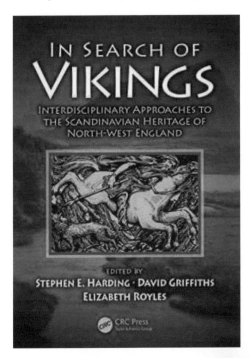

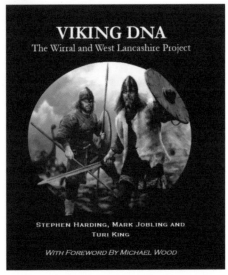

Please help to
Save St. Olave's Church

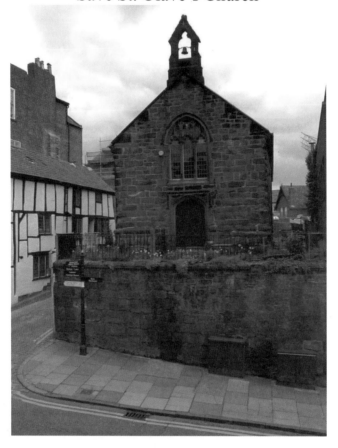

St. Olave's Church in Chester is a church dedicated to the patron saint of Norway and Scandinavia – St. Olav Haraldsson. It remains an important icon of our great Viking Heritage but is now under serious threat of being lost as its raised foundations are eroding away. In times of financial hardship, Government funding is not available to make the repairs and construction necessary to guarantee the survival of the church. If you can help in our efforts – including donations – please contact our Facebook site:
www.facebook.com/Save-Saint-Olaves-Church-Chester-304172436436130/
Even a statement of support would be appreciated!

STEPHEN ERNEST HARDING